Andrew Brodie Basics

LET'S DO HANDWRITING

FOR AGES 6-7

with over **100** reward stickers

- Structured practice of handwriting strokes
- Extra tips on style and tidiness
- Regular progress checks

Published 2014 by Bloomsbury Publishing Plc
50 Bedford Square, London, WC1B 3DP

www.bloomsbury.com

Bloomsbury is a registered trade mark of Bloomsbury Publishing Plc

ISBN 978-1-4729-1024-0

First published 2014
© 2014 Andrew Brodie
Cover and inside illustrations of Martha the Meerkat and Andrew Brodie © 2014 Nikalas Catlow
Other inside illustrations © 2014 Steve Evans

A CIP catalogue for this book is available from the British Library.

10 9 8 7 6 5 4 3

Printed in China by Leo Paper Products

This book is produced using paper that is made from wood grown in managed, sustainable forests. It is natural, renewable and recyclable. The logging and manufacturing process conform to the environmental regulations of the country of origin.

To see our full range of titles visit **www.bloomsbury.com**

BLOOMSBURY

Notes for parents

What's in this book

This is the second book in an exciting new series of *Andrew Brodie Basics: Let's Do Handwriting*. Each book features a clearly structured approach to developing and improving children's handwriting, an essential skill for correct spelling and effective written communication. Check the handwriting style used at your child's school as there are slight variations between schools. The style used in this book reflects the most popular one.

The National Curriculum states that during Key Stage 1, children should be encouraged to sit correctly at a table, holding a pencil with a comfortable and appropriate grip. Six to seven year olds learn to form lower-case letters, capital letters and digits of the correct size and relationship to one another; they learn to use appropriate spacing between words; they start to practise some of the diagonal and horizontal strokes needed to join letters but they recognize that some letters should remain unjoined at this stage.

How you can help

Make sure your child is ready for their handwriting practice by checking that their chair and table are of appropriate heights so that they are comfortable and can reach their work easily. They should be able to place this book flat on a desk or table and the work area should be a well-lit uncluttered space.

Your child should place the book at an appropriate angle so that their handwriting is clearly visible to them. If your child is left-handed, the book will need to be turned to the opposite angle to that used by right-handed people: it is essential that they can see their work, rather than covering it with their hand as they write.

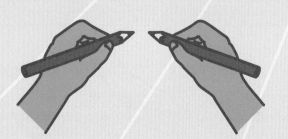

Martha the Meerkat

Look out for Martha the Meerkat, who tells your child what to focus on ready for the progress check at the end of each section.

Andrew Brodie says...

On some pages there are further tips and reminders from Andrew Brodie, which are devised to encourage your child to self-check their work.

When your child does well, makes sure you tell them so! The colourful stickers in the middle of this book can be a great reward for good work and a big incentive for future progress.

The answer section

The answer section at the back of this book can be a useful teaching tool: ask your child to compare their handwriting to the exemplars shown on the Progress Check 'answers'. If they have written their letters and words correctly, congratulate them, but if they haven't, don't let them worry about it! Instead, encourage them to learn the correct versions. Give lots of praise for any success.

Copy the letters carefully.

a   a   a   a

b   b   b   b

c   c   c   c

d   d   d   d

e   e   e   e

Now try smaller versions of the same letters.

a   a   a   a   a   a

b   b   b   b   b b

c   c   c   c   cc

d   d   d   d   d d

e   e   e   e   ee

Can you spot which letters have ascenders?

Andrew Brodie says...

Don't forget that the letters **b** and **d** are taller than the other letters.

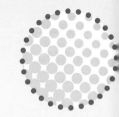

Copy the letters carefully.

f f f f f

g g g g

h h h h

i i i i

j j j j

Now try smaller versions of the same letters.

f f f f

g g g g

h h h h

i i i i

j j j j

Andrew Brodie says...
Don't forget that the letters
g and j have descenders.

Can you spot which letters have descenders?

4

Which of these letters have ascenders?

Copy the letters carefully.

k k k k k

l l l l l

m m m m m

n n n n n

o o o o o

Now try smaller versions of the same letters.

k k k k k

l l l l l

m m m m m

n n n n n

o o o o o

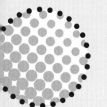

Andrew Brodie says...

Make sure that each letter sits neatly on the writing line and that the letters with ascenders are taller than the other letters.

Copy the letters carefully.

p p p p p

q q q q

r r r r

s s s s

t t t t t

Now try smaller versions of the same letters.

p p p p p

q q q q q

r r r r

s s s s

t t t t

Andrew Brodie says...
Make sure that each letter sits
neatly on the writing line and that the tails
of the descenders pass through the line.

Notice that letter **t**
is taller than most
of the other letters.

Practise u to z

Letter y has a descender.

Copy the letters carefully.

Now try smaller versions of the same letters.

7

Write each letter twice.
Try to keep them all the same size.

a	b	c	d	e
f	g	h	i	j
k	l	m	n	o
p	q	r	s	t
u	v	w	x	y z

Writing challenge ⟶

Write the letters of the alphabet all round the circle. You will need to turn the book around as you write. Can you keep every letter the same size?

a b c

Write these sentences as neatly as you can.

The toy zebra is kept in a large box.

We need to feed the animals very quickly.

Copy the letters carefully.

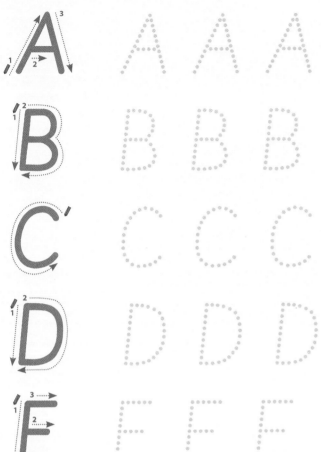

A A A A A A
B B B B B B
C C C C C C
D D D D D D
E E E E E E

Write the capital letters and the lower case letters together.

Aa Aa Aa Aa
Bb Bb Bb Bb
Cc Cc Cc Cc
Dd Dd Dd Dd
Ee Ee Ee Ee

Andrew Brodie says...

Don't forget that capital letters are as tall as letters with ascenders and that they are never joined.

Capital letters are used at the start of sentences.

Copy the letters carefully.

F F F F

G G G G

H H H H

I I I I

J J J J

Write the capital letters and the lower case letters together.

Ff Ff Ff Ff

Gg Gg Gg Gg

Hh Hh Hh Hh

Ii Ii Ii Ii

Jj Jj Jj Jj

Andrew Brodie says...

Make sure that the letters sit neatly on the line and that they are are as tall as the letters with ascenders.

10

Capital letters are used at the start of names.

Copy the letters carefully.

K K K K

L L L L

M M M M

N N N N

O O O O

Write the capital letters and the lower case letters together.

Kk Kk Kk Kk

Ll Ll Ll Ll

Mm Mm Mm Mm

Nn Nn Nn Nn

Oo Oo Oo Oo

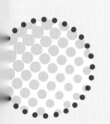

Andrew Brodie says...

Make sure you leave gaps between the pairs of letters.

Capital letters are used at the start of the names of days.

Copy the letters carefully.

P P P P P

Q Q Q Q

R R R R R

S S S S

T T T T T

Write the capital letters and the lower case letters together.

Pp Pp Pp Pp

Qq Qq Qq Qq

Rr Rr Rr Rr

Ss Ss Ss Ss

Tt Tt Tt Tt

Andrew Brodie says...
Don't forget that the capital letters are as tall as the ascenders.

Capital letters U to Z

Capital letters are used at the start of the names of months.

Copy the letters carefully.

U U U U

V V V V

W W W W

X X X X

Y Y Y Y

Z Z Z Z

Write the capital letters and the lower case letters together.

Uu Uu Uu Uu

Vv Vv Vv Vv

Ww Ww Ww Ww

Xx Xx Xx Xx

Yy Yy Yy Yy

Zz Zz Zz Zz

Write each letter twice.
Try to keep them all the same size.

A   B   C   D   E

F   G   H   I   J

K   L   M   N   O

P   Q   R   S   T

U   V   W   X   Y   Z

Writing challenge ⟶

Write the letters of the alphabet all round the circle. You will need to turn the book around as you write. Can you keep every letter the same size?

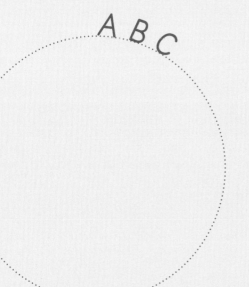

A B C

Write these names as neatly as possible.

Amber	Ben	Charlotte
Dylan	Evie	Finn
Georgia	Harvey	Isla
Jasdeep	Kayla	Luca
Muhammad		Noah
Olivia	Patrick	Quentin
Robyn	Seth	Tyler
Umar	Violet	Willow
Xander	Yara	Zara

Numbers 0 to 5

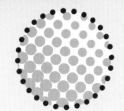

Did you know that the number **0** can be called zero or nought?

Copy the numbers carefully.

0   0   0   0

1   1   1   1

2   2   2   2

3   3   3   3

4   4   4   4

5   5   5   5

Write the words and numbers as neatly as you can.

0 zero   0 zero

1 one   1 one

2 two   2 two

3 three   3 three

4 four   4 four

5 five   5 five

Numbers 6 to 11

It is important to write numbers carefully and clearly.

Copy the numbers carefully.

6 6 6 6

7 7 7 7

8 8 8 8

9 9 9 9

10 10 10 10

11 11 11 11

Write the words and numbers as neatly as you can.

6 six   6 six

7 seven   7 seven

8 eight   8 eight

9 nine   9 nine

10 ten   10 ten

11 eleven   11 eleven

Words and numbers

Be careful when you write words and numbers.

Look carefully at the words on the list.

ninety   sixty   seventeen   twenty   thirteen   eighteen

fifteen   eighty   fourteen   forty   nineteen   thirty

twelve   sixteen   fifty   hundred   seventy

Write each word very carefully next to the correct number.

12	20
13	30
14	40
15	50
16	60
17	70
18	80
19	90
	100

Andrew Brodie says...
Make sure that your letters sit neatly on the line.

Numbers and words

Keep practising words and numbers.

Look carefully at the numbers in the number bank.

56 79 95 345 44
37 169 63 21 300
82 700 28 900

Write each number very carefully next to the correct word. Copy the words carefully.

eighty-two

forty-four

fifty-six

twenty-eight

thirty-seven

seventy-nine

ninety-five

sixty-three

three hundred and forty-five

three hundred

one hundred and sixty-nine

seven hundred

nine hundred

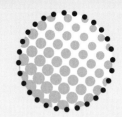

Copy the pound signs carefully.

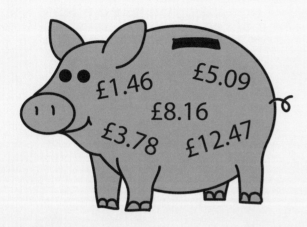

£1.46 £5.09
£8.16
£3.78 £12.47

> The pound sign and the question mark should be the same height as capital letters.

Write the correct amount of money using the pound sign and neat numbers for each amount shown below.

Three pounds seventy-eight pence

Twelve pounds forty-seven pence

One pound forty-six pence

Eight pounds sixteen pence

Five pounds and nine pence

Copy the question marks carefully.

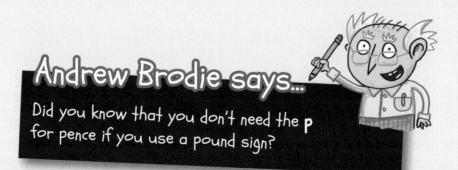

Andrew Brodie says...

Did you know that you don't need the **p** for pence if you use a pound sign?

Write each number three times.
Try to keep them all the same size.

0

1

2

3

4

5

6

7

8

9

Write a row of pound signs and a row of
question marks as neatly as possible.

£

?

Writing challenge

Write the numbers in the
correct places on the number
line. Can you keep every
number the same size?

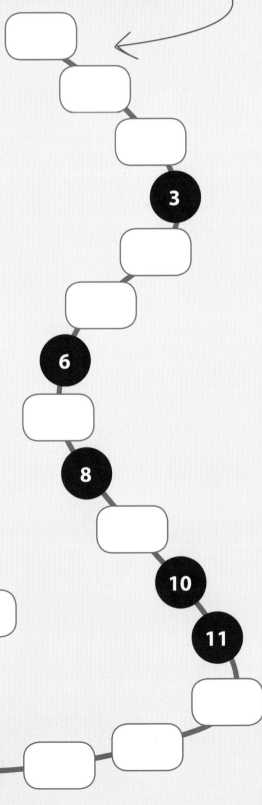

Joining the letter a

The joining line goes from the bottom of the letter **a** to the top of the next letter so we call it a slope join.

Trace over the joined letters then copy them.

an   an   an   an

am   am   am   am

ar   ar   ar   ar

ac   ac   ac   ac

ad   ad   ad   ad

Now try using the slope join with pairs of smaller letters.

aw   an   an   an

at   am   am   am

as   ar   ar   ar

ab   ac   ac   ac

ag   ad   ad   ad

al   ad   ad   ad

ao   ao   ao   ao

Andrew Brodie says...
Which of the pairs of letters above spell real words?

Trace over the joined letters then copy them.

ca   ca ca ca

co   co co co

ck   ck ck ck

cl   cl cl cl

cc   cc cc cc

Now try using the slope join with pairs of smaller letters.

ct   ct ct ct

ce   ce ce ce

ch   ch ch ch

ci   ci ci ci

cr   cr cr cr

cu   cu cu cu

Andrew Brodie says...

Make sure you work slowly and carefully. Don't press too hard on the paper.

Joining letter d

Trace over the joined letters then copy them.

da   da da da

do   do do do

de   de de de

di   di di di

du   du du du

Now try using the slope join with pairs of smaller letters.

dd   dd dd dd

dm   dm dm dm

dv   dv dv dv

dw   dw dw dw

dy   dy dy dy

dn   dn dn dn

Andrew Brodie says...

Make sure that the letter **d** is taller than the other letters and that you use a clear slope join.

We always use a slope join from a letter **d**.

23

> We always use a slope join from a letter **h**.

Trace over the joined letters then copy them.

ha _ha ha_

he _he he_

hi _hi hi_

ho _ho ho_

hu _hu hu_

Now try using the slope join with pairs of smaller letters.

head _head head_

hid _hid hid_

hand _hand hand_

heap _heap heap_

hide _hide hide_

sand _sand sand_

side _side side_

Andrew Brodie says...

Did you notice that the letter **s** is not joined to the letters that follow it?

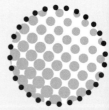

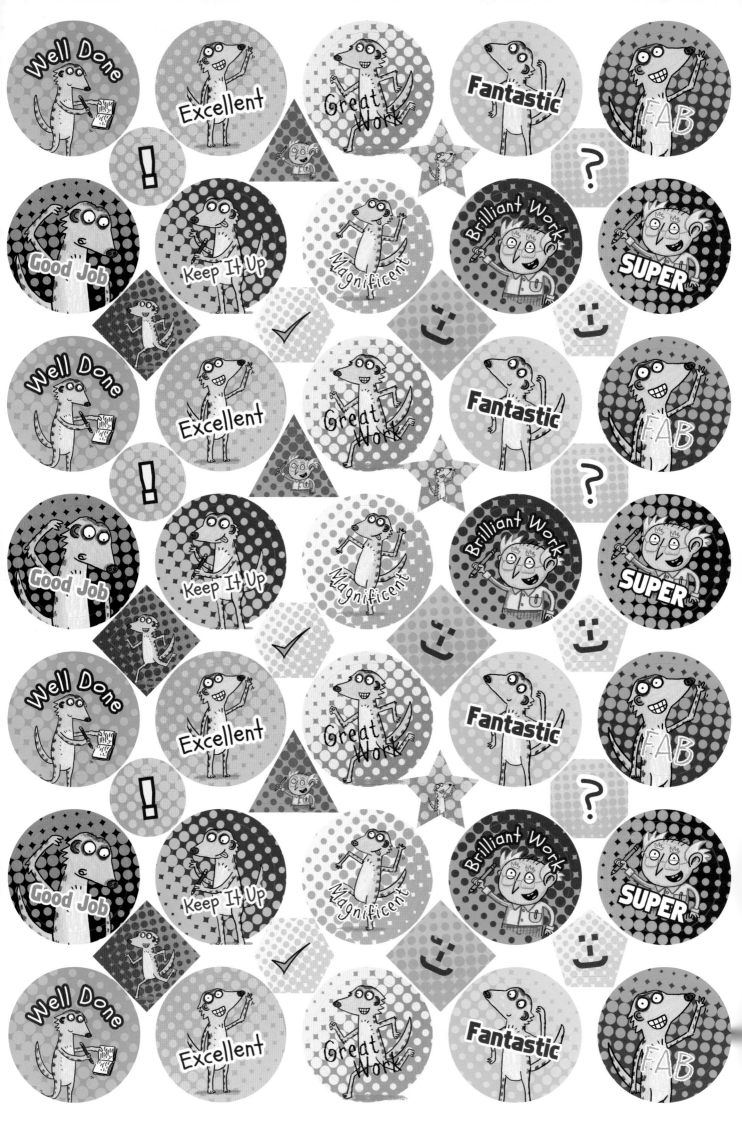

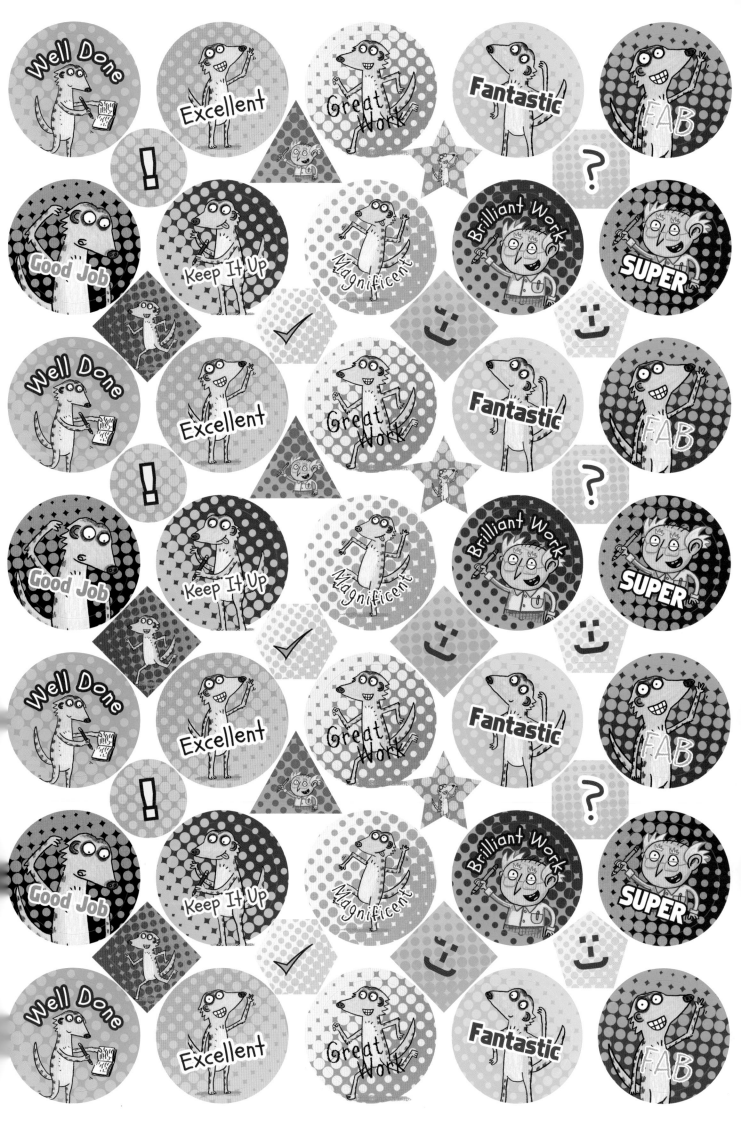

We always use a slope join from a letter **e**.

Trace over the joined letters then copy them.

ea   ea   ea

eb   eb   eb

ec   ec   ec

ed   ed   ed

ee   ee   ee

Now try using the slope join with these words:

east   east east

ear   ear ear

easy   easy easy

edit   edit edit

edible   edible edible

egg   egg egg

echo   echo echo

Andrew Brodie says...

Did you notice that the letters **b**, **g** and **s** are not joined to the letters that follow them?

25

Write each pair of letters three times. Try to keep them all the same size. Don't forget to use slope joins.

ac

ah

ca

co

du

di

hy

ee

ep

Write each of these words five times as neatly as possible.

ace

dear

cheer

chase

cheap

deep

hide

cash

dash

> The joining line goes from the top of the letter **o** to the top of the next letter, so we call it a bridge join.

Trace over the joined letters then copy them.

op   op   op

on   on   on

oa   oa   oa

oc   oc   oc

or   or   or

ow   ow   ow

Now try using slope joins and bridge joins with these words:

coat   coat   coat

count   count   count

hoop   hoop   hoop

cow   cow   cow

done   done   done

moon   moon   moon

soon   soon   soon

Joining the letter w

The joining line goes from the top of the letter **w** to the top of the next letter so it is a bridge join.

Trace over the joined letters then copy them.

wo   wo   wo

wa   wa   wa

wi   wi   wi

wu   wu   wu

we   we   we

Now try using slope joins and bridge joins with these words:

want   want   want

went   went   went

won't   won't   won't

weed   weed   weed

wider   wider   wider

weather   weather   weather

owl   owl   owl

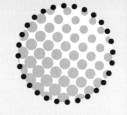

Joining the letter v

Trace over the joined letters then copy them.

va   va va

ve   ve ve

vi   vi vi

vo   vo vo

vu   vu vu

Now try using slope joins and bridge joins with these words:

van   van van

oven   oven oven

over   over over

wove   wove wove

wave   wave wave

save   save save

vehicle   vehicle vehicle

The joining line goes from the top of the letter **v** to the top of the next letter, so it is a bridge join.

The joining line goes from the end of the letter r to the start of the next letter. It is a bridge join.

Trace over the joined letters then copy them.

ra   ra   ra

re   re   re

ri   ri   ri

ro   ro   ro

ru   ru   ru

Now try using slope joins and bridge joins with these words:

red   red   red

real   real   real

rest   rest   rest

radio   radio   radio

care   care   care

carry   carry   carry

carried   carried   carried

Joining the letter f

Look carefully at how we join from a letter **f**.

Trace over the joined letters then copy them.

fa   fa   fa

fe   fe   fe

fi   fi   fi

fo   fo   fo

fu   fu   fu

Now try using slope joins and bridge joins with these words:

for   for   for

four   four   four

often   often   often

father   father   father

feather   feather   feather

faster   faster   faster

finger   finger   finger

Write each pair of letters three times. Try to keep them all the same size. Don't forget to use bridge joins.

on

of

we

ow

vi

vu

ro

ri

fi

fe

Write each of these words five times as neatly as possible.

once

twice

serve

sweet

fire

office

very

every

after

Letter b

We don't always join from a letter **b**.

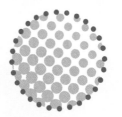

Trace over the words then copy them.

boy   boy

band   band

able   able

boat   boat

baby   baby

Now try using slope joins and bridge joins with these words:

table   table

tablet   tablet

cable   cable

stable   stable

rabbit   rabbit

hobby   hobby

lobby   lobby

We don't always join from a letter g

Trace over the words then copy them.

girl girl

go go

got got

bigger bigger

bags bags

Now try using slope joins and bridge joins with these words:

huge huge

garden garden

singing singing

bringing bringing

goggles goggles

gobble gobble

leggings leggings

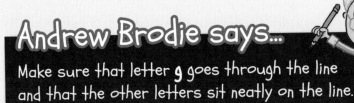

Andrew Brodie says...

Make sure that letter g goes through the line
and that the other letters sit neatly on the line.

Letter p

Like the letter **g**, the letter **p** has a descender.

Trace over the words then copy them.

park   park

spark   spark

rope   rope

hope   hope

soaps   soaps

Now try using slope joins and bridge joins with these words:

apple   apple

ripple   ripple

simple   simple

please   please

supper   supper

repeat   repeat

steeper   steeper

Andrew Brodie says...

Make sure that letter **p** goes through the line
and that the other letters sit neatly on the line.

Letters q and u

We don't always join from a letter **q**. Letter **q** is always followed by a letter **u**.

Trace over the words then copy them.

quit quit

quad quad

quiz quiz

quite quite

quiet quiet

Now try using slope joins and bridge joins with these words:

square square

quarter quarter

queen queen

enquire enquire

require require

squid squid

squat squat

Andrew Brodie says...

Make sure that letter **q** goes through the line.
Make sure that the other letters sit neatly on the line.

Letters y and j

We don't always join from a letter **y** or a letter **j**. These letters have descenders.

Trace over the words then copy them.

you   you

yes   yes

yell   yell

year   year

jelly   jelly

Now try using slope joins and bridge joins with these words:

yellow   yellow

yesterday   yesterday

judge   judge

major   major

join   join

jolly   jolly

joiner   joiner

Andrew Brodie says...

Make sure that letter **j** and the letter **y** go through the line and that the other letters sit neatly on the line.

37

Write each word five times. Try to keep the letters all the same size. Don't forget that letters with ascenders are taller and that letters with descenders go through the line.

red

orange

yellow

green

blue

indigo

violet

pink

purple

brown

black

white

| elephant | lion | tiger | giraffe | crocodile |

Write the correct word with each picture. Use slope joins, bridge joins and remember which letters don't join.

Questions and answers

Can you write questions and answers in your best handwriting?

How old are you?

No, it is sunny today.

What day is my birthday this year?

I am seven years old.

Is it raining?

It will be on a Saturday.

Write each question, then write the correct answer.

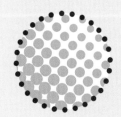

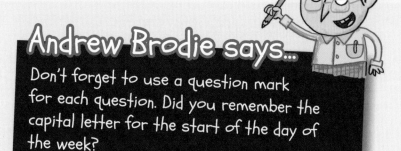

Andrew Brodie says...

Don't forget to use a question mark for each question. Did you remember the capital letter for the start of the day of the week?

More questions and answers

Can you use your best handwriting?

What is the capital city of Scotland?

The capital city of England is London.

The capital city of Wales is Cardiff.

What is the capital city of England?

The capital city of Scotland is Edinburgh.

What is the capital city of Wales?

Write each question, then write the correct answer.

Andrew Brodie says...

Don't forget the capital letters for the start of each name of place. Remember to write a capital letter at the start of each question.

40

Question words

Copy each of these words five times.

what

where

why

who

when

which

how

Write two questions of your own. You can start each question using one of the words from above, or you can start with a different word of your own.

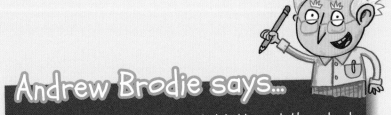
41

Rhyme time

Copy each rhyme using your best handwriting.

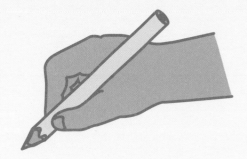

Use your hands, not both feet,
So your writing is neat.

Taking care with each letter
Makes your writing much better.

Rhyme time

Copy the rhyme using your best handwriting.

Jack and Jill went up the hill
To practise their best writing.
Jack fell then,
And broke his pen,
And Jill thought it very exciting.

Andrew Brodie says...

Does your rhyme look neat and tidy?
Did you remember to write a capital letter
at the start of each line?

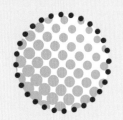

Write each question, then write the correct answer.

In which month do the school holidays start?

How old will you be on your next birthday?

I will be eight years old.

The holidays start in July.

How much is that packet of sweets?

It costs £1.93.

Copy the rhyme very carefully.

Mary had a little lamb,
She taught it how to write.
It wasn't very difficult
As the little lamb was bright.

ANSWERS

Talk about the progress checks with your child, encouraging him/her to match each one with the copies shown here.

Andrew Brodie says...

Check the following:
- Are the letters consistent in size?
- Does your child remember to make the tall letters taller than the other letters?
- Do the letters sit neatly on the writing lines?
- Do the letters such as g j p and y go through the line?
- Are the letters i and j written correctly?
- Have they each got a dot?

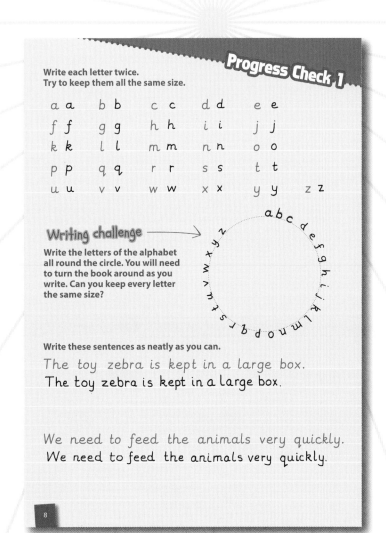

Progress Check 1

Write each letter twice.
Try to keep them all the same size.

a a   b b   c c   d d   e e
f f   g g   h h   i i   j j
k k   l l   m m   n n   o o
p p   q q   r r   s s   t t
u u   v v   w w   x x   y y   z z

Writing challenge

Write the letters of the alphabet all round the circle. You will need to turn the book around as you write. Can you keep every letter the same size?

Write these sentences as neatly as you can.

The toy zebra is kept in a large box.
The toy zebra is kept in a large box.

We need to feed the animals very quickly.
We need to feed the animals very quickly.

8

Write each letter twice.
Try to keep them all the same size.

A A A   B B B   C C C   D D D   E E E
F F F   G G G   H H H   I I I   J J J
K K K   L L L   M M M   N N N   O O O
P P P   Q Q Q   R R R   S S S   T T T
U U U   V V V   W W W   X X X   Y Y Y   Z Z Z

Writing challenge

Write the letters of the alphabet all round the circle. You will need to turn the book around as you write. Can you keep every letter the same size?

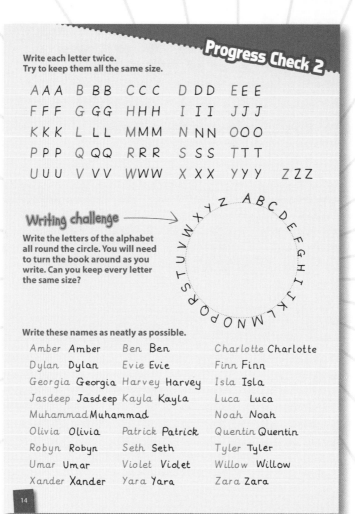

Write these names as neatly as possible.

Amber Amber   Ben Ben   Charlotte Charlotte
Dylan Dylan   Evie Evie   Finn Finn
Georgia Georgia   Harvey Harvey   Isla Isla
Jasdeep Jasdeep   Kayla Kayla   Luca Luca
Muhammad Muhammad   Noah Noah
Olivia Olivia   Patrick Patrick   Quentin Quentin
Robyn Robyn   Seth Seth   Tyler Tyler
Umar Umar   Violet Violet   Willow Willow
Xander Xander   Yara Yara   Zara Zara

14

Write each number three times.
Try to keep them all the same size.

0   0 0 0
1   1 1 1
2   2 2 2
3   3 3 3
4   4 4 4
5   5 5 5
6   6 6 6
7   7 7 7
8   8 8 8
9   9 9 9

Write a row of pound signs and a row of question marks as neatly as possible.

£   £ £ £
?   ? ? ?

Writing challenge

Write the numbers in the correct places on the number line. Can you keep every number the same size?

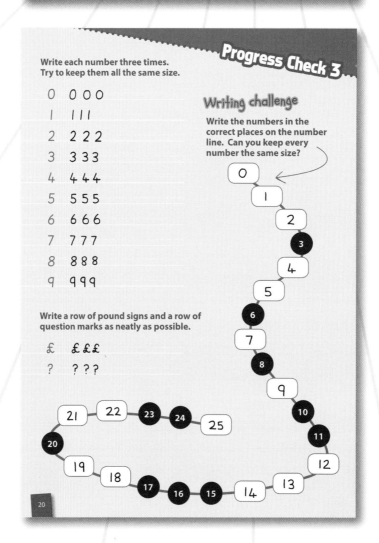

20

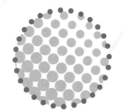

Write each pair of letters three times. Try to
keep them all the same size. Don't forget to use slope joins.

ac ac ac ac
ah ah ah ah
ca ca ca ca
co co co co
du du du du
di di di di
hy hy hy hy
ee ee ee ee
ep ep ep ep

Write each of these words five times as neatly as possible.

ace ace ace ace ace ace
dear dear dear dear dear dear
cheer cheer cheer cheer cheer cheer
chase chase chase chase chase chase
cheap cheap cheap cheap cheap cheap
deep deep deep deep deep deep
hide hide hide hide hide hide
cash cash cash cash cash cash
dash dash dash dash dash dash

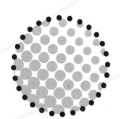

Write each pair of letters three times. Try to
keep them all the same size. Don't forget to use bridge joins.

on on on on
of of of of
we we we we
ow ow ow ow
vi vi vi vi
vu vu vu vu
ro ro ro ro
ri ri ri ri
fi fi fi fi
fe fe fe fe

Write each of these words five times as neatly as possible.

once once once once once once
twice twice twice twice twice twice
serve serve serve serve serve serve
sweet sweet sweet sweet sweet sweet
fire fire fire fire fire fire
office office office office office office
very very very very very very
every every every every every every
after after after after after after

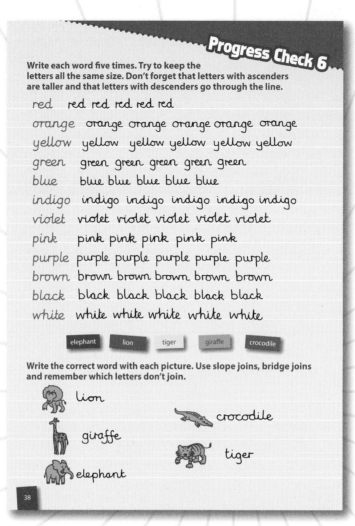

Write each word five times. Try to keep the
letters all the same size. Don't forget that letters with ascenders
are taller and that letters with descenders go through the line.

red   red red red red red

orange   orange orange orange orange orange

yellow   yellow yellow yellow yellow yellow

green   green green green green green

blue   blue blue blue blue blue

indigo   indigo indigo indigo indigo indigo

violet   violet violet violet violet violet

pink   pink pink pink pink pink

purple   purple purple purple purple purple

brown   brown brown brown brown brown

black   black black black black black

white   white white white white white

| elephant | lion | tiger | giraffe | crocodile |

Write the correct word with each picture. Use slope joins, bridge joins
and remember which letters don't join.

lion

crocodile

giraffe

tiger

elephant

38

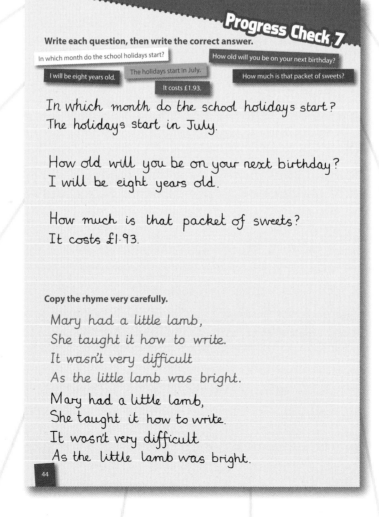

Write each question, then write the correct answer.

In which month do the school holidays start?		How old will you be on your next birthday?
I will be eight years old.	The holidays start in July.	How much is that packet of sweets?
	It costs £1.93.	

In which month do the school holidays start?
The holidays start in July.

How old will you be on your next birthday?
I will be eight years old.

How much is that packet of sweets?
It costs £1·93.

Copy the rhyme very carefully.

Mary had a little lamb,
She taught it how to write.
It wasn't very difficult
As the little lamb was bright.

Mary had a little lamb,
She taught it how to write.
It wasn't very difficult
As the little lamb was bright.

44